The Singer's Worship Series

A Seven-Year Collection

**Contemporary Christian Music
Arranged for the Church and Family**

**Compiled and Arranged by Ken Young
Recorded by the Hallal Singers**

Related Materials
(Cassettes, CDs)

"ALMIGHTY" SWS I

"MAJESTY" SWS II

"GLORY" SWS III

"FAITHFUL" SWS IV

"WORTHY" SWS V

"BEST OF..." SWS I–V

"RICHLY BLEST" SWS VI

Deeper Life Ministries   11-13-02 $7.96

D1208192

*The Singer's Worship Series began
because of the growing hunger
for new songs in the church.
Throughout history God has used
the power of music
to awaken the hearts of His people.
Though we have many great songs from our past,
there is something about an infinitely creative God
that causes us to continually seek Him
in new and refreshing ways.*

*Many of the songs in this collection
were birthed from the
inexhaustible fountain of life
flowing through the Word of God.
May God continue to open our eyes and our hearts
as we find ourselves lost in wonder and praise.
To Him be the glory for ever and ever!*

Table of Contents

1   Almighty

Words and Music by
Wayne Watson

Luke 19:40

Al-migh-ty,   Most Ho-ly God,   Faith-ful thru the a-ges;

Al - migh-ty,

Al-migh-ty,   Most Ho-ly Lord,   glor-i-ous, Al-migh-ty God.

Al - migh-ty,

1. The beasts   of   the field, the   birds of   the   air,   are
2. Well time march-es   on, with the   in - no - cence gone,   and a

si - lent   to   call out   your   name.   The
dark - ness   has   cov - ered   the   earth.   But his

earth has   no voice,   and   I   have   no choice,   but to
Spir - it   still dwells,   he   speaks, "It   is   well."   and the

Arranged by Ken Young

As the Deer

Words and Music by
Martin Nystrom

Psalm 42:1,2

1. As the deer pants for the wa-ter so my soul longs af-ter
2. I want you more than gold or sil-ver, on-ly you can sat-is-

you. You a-lone are my heart's de-sire and I long to wor-ship
fy. You a-lone are the real joy-giv-er, and the ap-ple of my

you. You a-lone are my strength, my shield; to you a-lone may my
eye.

spir-it yield. You a-lone are my

heart's de-sire and I long to wor-ship you. you.

Holy Ground

3

Words and Music by
Christopher Beatty

Exodus 3:5

1. This is ho - ly ground, we're stand - ing on
*2. You are ho - ly, God. a per - fect and

ho - ly ground. For the Lord is pres - ent and where He is is
ho - ly God. We will come be - fore you with hearts made clean by

ho - ly. This is ho - ly ground, we're stand - ing on
Je - sus' blood. You are ho - ly, God. a per - fect and

ho - ly ground. For the Lord is pres - ent and
ho - ly God. We will come be - fore you with

where He is is ho - ly.
hearts made clean by Je - sus' blood.

*Words by Ken Young

4

Holy Ground

Genesis 28:17

Words and Music by
Geron Davis

We are stand-ing on ho-ly ground. And I know that there are an-gels all a-round. Let us praise Je-sus now; We are stand-ing in His

1. pres-ence on ho-ly ground.

2. pres-ence; we are stand-ing in His pres-ence; We are stand-ing in His pres-ence on ho-ly ground.

In His Presence

5

Psalm 16:11

Words and Music by
Dick & Melodie Tunney

In His pres - ence there is com - fort, In His
pres - ence there is peace. When we
seek the Fa - ther's heart we will find such bless'd as -
sur - ance, in the pres - ence of the Lord.
Lord. Cov - er me, Lord, with Your pres - ence.

6 All Rise

Words and Music by
Babbie Mason

Revelation 4,5

1. There was a ho - ly hush all o - ver as I
2. As I looked at those a - round me with their

walked in - to the room, and I as stood be - fore Him face to face was I
hands up - lift - ed high, the Spir - it laid His hands on me and

glor - ious - ly made new. There was a great and awe - some pres - ence, and the
I up - lift - ed mine. We were sing - ing hal - le - lu - jah,

light bright as the day. And as I bowed to kneel with an - gels I
prais - es to His name.

heard the Spir - it say, "All

7   Great and Marvelous

Revelation 15:3,4

Music by
Ken Young

Great and mar-ve-lous are your deeds, Lord, God Al-migh-ty. Just and

true are your ways, King of the Ag-es. Who'll not fear you, O

Lord, and bring glo-ry to your name? For you a-lone are ho-

ly. All na-tions will come and wor-ship be-fore you;

for you a-lone are ho-ly, for your right-eous acts have been re-vealed!

Son of Man

Revelation 1:12-18

Words and Music by
Ken Young

1. Re - gal robe, gold - en sash; hair so white with eyes like fire.
2. Sev - en lamp - stands, sev - en stars; from his mouth a two - edged sword.

Feet like bronze, glow - ing bright; voice so pure and filled with power.
Face is shin - ing like the sun; Sov' - reign King and Migh - ty Lord.

Son of Man, Son of Man, I fall at the feet of the Son of Man. He
Son of Man,

lifts me up and he helps me stand in the ho - ly pres - ence

of the Son of Man; in the daz - zling pres - ence of the Son of Man.

9　Turn Your Eyes Upon Jesus

Words and Music by
Helen H. Lemmel

Psalm 27:8

Turn your eyes up-on Je - sus, look full in His

won - der- ful face.　And the things of earth will grow
won - der- ful　face.

strange - ly dim, in the light of His glo - ry and grace.

2. And the things of earth will grow strange - ly dim, in the

light of His glo - ry and grace.

Victory Chant

Revelation 5:5

Words and Music by
Joseph Vogels

Hail, Je - sus, you're my King, your life frees me to sing;

I will praise you all my days, you're per - fect in all your ways.

Hail, Je - sus, you're my Lord, I will o - bey your word; I

want to see your king- dom come, not my will but your's be done.

Glo- ry, glo - ry to the Lamb, lead us with your migh- ty hand;

We will con- quer in your name, and pro - claim that Je - sus reigns.

Hail, hail, Lion of Ju - dah, how pow - er - ful you are;

Lord, God, strong and migh- ty, how won - der- ful you are.

Arranged by Ken Young

11   Above All Else

Philippians 2:9

Words and Music by
Kirk Dearman

You are ex-alt-ed, Lord, a-bove all else;

we place you at the high-est place, a-bove all else.

Right now where we stand and ev'-ry-where we go;

we place you at the high-est place so the world will know.

You are a migh-ty war-ri-or, dressed in ar-mor of light;

Arranged by Ken Young

crush-ing the deeds of dark-ness, lead us on in the fight.

Through the blood of Je - sus, vic - tor - i - ous we stand.

We place you at the high-est place, a - bove all else in this

1. 2. *Second time D.S.* | 3.

land. land. a - bove all else.

12   I Love You, Lord

Words and Music by
Laurie Klein

Psalm 40:16

I love you, Lord, and I lift my voice to wor-ship you, O my soul, re-joice! Take joy, my King, in what you hear; may it be a sweet, sweet sound in your ear.

Glorify Thy Name

13

Psalm 86:12

Words and Music by
Donna Adkins

1. Fa - ther,
2. Je - sus, we love you, we wor - ship and a - dore you.
3. Spir- it,

Glo - ri - fy thy name in all the earth.

Glo - ri - fy thy name, glo - ri - fy thy name.

Glo - ri - fy thy name in all the earth.

14 The Name of God

Psalm 29:2

Words and Music by
Ken Young

Speak the name of God so sol-emn-ly, speak the name of God in prayer. In a world so full of pro-fan-i-ty, speak the name of God with care. El El-yon, the God of Is-ra-el; El Shad-dai, the God of the Moun-tain. Lord of Hosts, and Right-eous Fa-ther; we glo-ri-fy the Great I Am!

15 Not To Us

Music by
Ken Young

Psalm 115:1

Not to us, O Lord, not to us, but to your name be the glo - ry be - cause of your love and your faith-ful-ness; O love and your faith - ful - ness.

Jesus, Name Above All Names 16

Philippians 2:9

Words and Music by
Naida Hearn

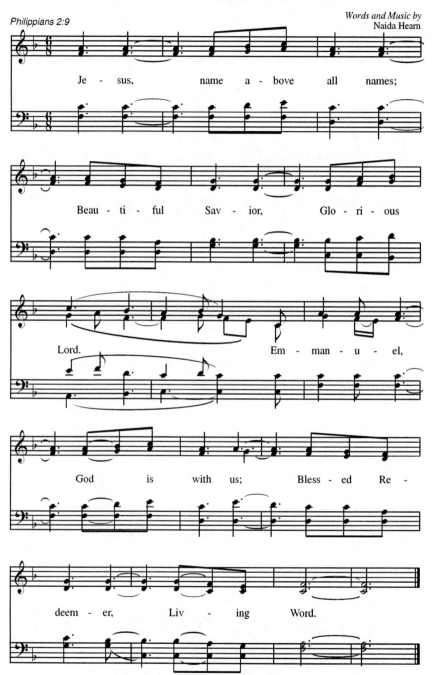

Je-sus, name a-bove all names;

Beau - ti - ful Sav - ior, Glo - ri - ous

Lord. Em - man - u - el,

God is with us; Bless - ed Re -

deem - er, Liv - ing Word.

17   Amazing Grace

Romans 5:1-5

Words and Music by
John Newton

(sop.) 1. A - maz - ing grace! how sweet the sound! That
(add altos) 2. 'Twas grace that taught my heart to fear, And
(add men) 3. Thro' man - y dan - gers, toils, and snares, I

saved a wretch like me! *(O re-lieved)* I once was
grace my fears re - lieved. *(O re-lieved)* How pre - cious
have al - read - y come. *(al-read-y come)* 'Tis grace hath

lost, but now am found; Was blind but now I
did that grace ap - pear the hour I first be -
brought me safe thus far; And grace will lead me

1. 2. see.
lieved.
3. home.

4. When we've been

Arranged by Ken Young

there   ten   thou - sand   years;   Bright,   shin - ing   as   the

sun. *(as the sun)* We've   no   less   days   to   sing   God's   praise   than

when   we   first   be - gun.

18　We Declare That the Kingdom of God Is Here

Matthew 10:7

Words and Music by
Graham Kendrick

(women echo) We de-clare that the king-dom of God is here,

we de-clare that the king-dom of God is here a-mong you, a-mong you.

(together) The blind see, the deaf hear, the lame men are walk-ing,

sick-ness-es flee at His voice; The dead live a-gain and the

poor hear the good news, Je-sus is King, so re-joice.

We de-clare that the king-dom of God is here,

we de-clare that the king-dom of God is here!

Arranged by Ken Young

Consider Him

19

Hebrews 12:1-3

Words and Music by
Ken Young

1. Sur-round-ed by those who have trav-eled this road, we throw off the heav-y and hin-der-ing load. The sin that en-tang-les we lay it a-side, and run with our eyes on the one cru-ci-fied.

2. The au-thor and per-fec-ter of our faith paid the cost, for the joy set be-fore him he suf-fered the cross. Scorn-ing its shame he sat down by the throne, and smiled as he watched his lost chil-dren come home.

Con-si-der him, who en-dured such op-po-si-tion from sin-ful men. Con-si-der him, so that you will not grow wea-ry and lose heart. Con-si-der him, con-si-der him.

Con-si-der
Con-si-der

(On 2nd verse, repeat last phrase 3 times.)

20 Lamb of God

Words and Music by
Twila Paris

John 1:29

Slowly 1. { Your on - ly Son, no sin to hide, but you have
{ Your gift of love they cru - ci - fied, they laughed and
Faster 2. I was so lost, I should have died, but you have

sent him from your side, to walk up - on this guilt - y
scorned him as he died; the hum - ble King they named a
brought me to your side, to be led by your staff and

sod, and to be - come the Lamb of God.
fraud, and sac - ri - ficed the Lamb of God.
rod, and to be called a lamb of God.

Lamb of

Refrain

O Lamb of God, sweet Lamb of God, I love the ho - ly Lamb of

God! O wash me in His pre - cious blood, my Je - sus Christ the Lamb of God.

Arranged by Ken Young

Lamb of

Worthy Is the Lamb 21

Revelation 5:9-14

Words and Music by
John G. Elliot

1. He pur-chased men with pre-cious blood; from ev'-ry na-tion, tribe and tongue. Bought from slav'-ry, freed from pri-son chains. Brought through death that they might rise a-gain; born to serve and to reign.

2. Ho-ly, ho-ly to our God; who was, who is, who is to come. Let us join the throng who see his face. Bow-ing down to him both night and day; lost in won-der and praise.

Wor-thy is the Lamb who was slain to re-ceive high-est

1. hon-or, and glo-ry, and pow-er, and praise.

2. hon-or, and glo-ry, and praise.

Arranged by Ken Young

22   Christ, We Do All Adore You

Words and Music by
Th. Baker & Th. Dubots

Revelation 5:9

Christ we do all adore you, and we do praise you for-ev - er.

ev - er. For on the ho - ly cross you died to
For on the

crush the pow'rs of dark - ness. Christ, we do all a -

dore you, and we do praise you for - ev - er. We a -

dore you! We a - dore you! We a - dore you!

Arranged by Ken Young

Amen, and Amen

23

Music by
Ken Young

Revelation 7:12

A - men, A - men,

A - men, A - men,

A - men, A - men, A - men!

A - men, and A - men, and A - men, and A - men!

Fine

A - men, A - men, A - men!

A - men, and A - men, A - men, and A - men!

Praise and glo - ry, and wis - dom, and thanks,

Praise, wis - dom, thanks,

and hon - or, and pow - er, and strength

hon - or, pow - er, strength

D.C. al Fine

be to our God, for - e - ver and e - ver, A - men, and A - men!

24 Hymn of Glory

Revelation 19:1

Words and Music by
Charles Christmas

Glo - ry, Hal - le - lu - jah.
Glo - ry, ho - nor, strength and pow'r be - long to our Al - migh - ty God!

Glo - ry, Hal - le - lu - jah.
Glo - ry to the King of Kings, His ra - diance fills the earth.

1. Give thanks to our God and let Him be praised, with
2. His Word ev - er true, the Son of His love.
3. Wor - thy the Lamb who was slain for our sins. He

sanc - ti - fied hearts and hands that are raised.
Sing men of earth to the heav - ens a - bove.
laid down His life, He rose up a - gain.

Come join a song of praise to our King.
Ho - nor and glo - ry be - long to our God.
To us He gives un - end - ing life.

Arranged by Ken Young

Awesome God

25

Revelation 15:3

Words and Music by
Rich Mullins

Our God is an awe-some God; He reigns from

hea-ven a-bove with wis-dom, pow'r, and love. Our

1. 2.   3.

God is an awe-some God! God! Our

God is an awe-some God! Our God is an awe-some God!

Arranged by Ken Young

26   Awesome Power

Job 9:4-11

Words and Music by
John G. Elliot

Awe - some pow - er, bound - less grace. None can
fath - om all your ways. Truth and love are found in your
heart a - lone, right - eous - ness a - round your throne.
Ho - ly, Ho - ly, Ho - ly Lord, Most High.
Ho - ly, Ho - ly, Ho - ly Lord, Most High. Awe - some High.

Arranged by Ken Young

Be Exalted, O God

27

Psalm 57:9-11

Music by
Ken Young

I will praise you, O Lord, a - mong the na - tions; I will

sing of you a - mong the peo - ples. For great is your love, reach-

ing to the heav - ens; your faith - ful - ness reach - es to the skies.

Be ex - alt - ed, O God, a - bove the heav - ens, let your

1. glo-ry be o - ver all the earth.

2. glo - ry be o - ver all the earth.

28 Majesty

Psalm 93:1-2

Words and Music by
Jack W. Hayford

Maj - es - ty, wor - ship His maj - es - ty. Un - to

Je - sus be all glo - ry, pow - er and praise.

Maj - es - ty, King - dom au - thor - i - ty, flow from His

throne un - to His own, His an - them raise. So ex -

alt, lift up on high the name of Je - sus. Mag - ni -

Arranged by Ken Young

fy, come glo - ri - fy Christ Je - sus the King.

Maj - es - ty, wor - ship His maj - es - ty. Je - sus who

died, now glo - ri - fied, King of all Kings. Je - sus who

died, now glo - ri - fied, King of all Kings.

29 The Voice of the Lord

Psalm 29:3-8

Music by
Ken Young

The voice of the Lord is o - ver the wa - ters, the God of all glo - ry thun - ders. The voice of the Lord is filled with pow - er, the voice of the Lord is maj - es - tic. The voice of the Lord breaks the ce - dars of Le - ba - non; he makes her skip like a calf. The voice of the Lord strikes with

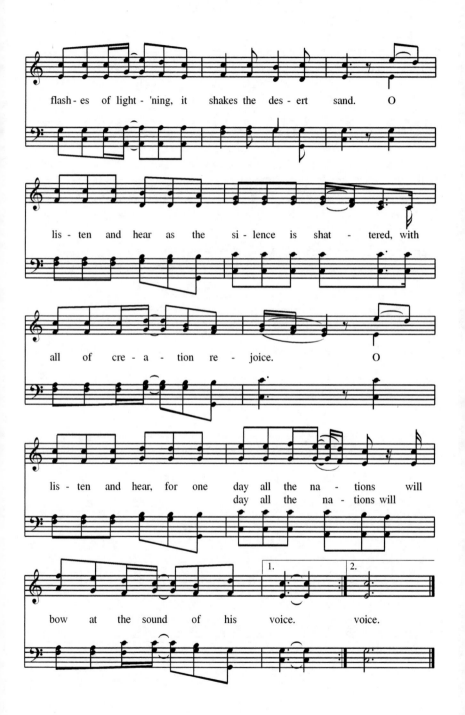

30 He Is Exalted

Psalm 18:46

Words and Music by
Twila Paris

He is ex-alt-ed, the King is ex-alt-ed on high; I will praise Him. He is ex-alt-ed, for-ev-er ex-alt-ed, and I will praise His name! He is the Lord; for-ev-er His truth shall reign. Heav-en and earth re-joice in His ho-ly name.

1. He is ex-alt-ed, the King is ex-alt-ed on high.

2. high.

Arranged by Ken Young

We Will Glorify

31

Words and Music by
Twila Paris

Isaiah 24:14-16a

1. We will glo - ri - fy the King of Kings, we will
2. Lord Je - ho - vah reigns in maj - es - ty, we will
3. He is Lord of heav - en, Lord of earth, He is
4. Hal - le - lu - jah to the King of Kings, Hal - le -

glo - ri - fy the Lamb. We will glo - ri - fy the
bow be - fore his throne. We will wor - ship him in
Lord of all who live. He is Lord a - bove the
lu - jah to the Lamb. Hal - le - lu - jah to the

1. 2. 3.   4.

Lord of Lords, who is the Great I AM!
right - eous - ness, we will wor - ship him a - lone.
u - ni - verse, all praise to him we give. 4. Oh,
Lord of Lords, who is the Great I   AM!

32   May the Words of My Mouth

Psalm 19:14

Words and Music by
Ken Young

May the words of my mouth and the med-i-ta-tion of my heart be pleas-ing in your sight, O Lord, my Rock and my Re-deem-er. May the words of my mouth and the med-i-ta-tion of my heart be pleas-ing in your sight, O Lord, my Rock and my Re-deem-er.

1. Liv - ing in a world so torn by Sa - tan's mas - quer - ad -
2. Drift - ing through this world in vague and thought - less in - di - rec -

ing leaves a bro - ken heart - ed peo - ple search - ing for
tion leaves a mind too weak and em - pty for the bat -

a sign of light. Lord, help me sing the words of praise that
tle of the heart. Lord, Je - sus fill my mind with all the

touch the trib - u - la - ting; the words that lift the
treas - ures you have gi - ven; the ar - mor you have

Sa - vior up and lead the blind to sight.
fit - ted to de - flect the flam - ing dart.

33   Rider On the White Horse

Revelation 19:11-16

Music and Words by
Ken Young

Rid-er on the white horse, rid-er called Faith-ful and True; with
jus-tice he judg-es and makes war. His eyes are like blaz - ing
fi - re, and on his head are man-y crowns;
rid - er on the white horse.

1. He has a name writ-ten on him, that no one but
2. Out his of mouth comes a sharp sword, with which to strike down the

he him-self knows; he is dressed in a robe
na - tions; he'll rule them with an

dipped in blood, and his name is the Word of God. The
iron scep - ter, and his name is the Word of God. He

arm-ies of heav - en were fol-low-ing him, rid-ing on white
treads the wine-press the of fu - ry, of the wrath of God Al -

hors - es; dressed in fine lin - en, white and clean, and his
migh - ty; on his robe and on his thigh, his

name is the Word is the Word of God!
name is writ-ten, King of Kings, and Lord of Lords!

34 Unto the King Eternal

Words and Music by
John G. Elliot

1 Timothy 1:17

Un-to the King e-ter-nal, un-to the King im-mor-tal, un-to the King in-vis-i-

ble, God on-ly wise.   ble, God on-ly wise.   Be   hon-or and be

glo-ry un-to   him,   un-to him. Be   hon-or and be   glo-ry un-to

him. For   -   ev - er,   and ev - er,   for - ev - er and   a -

men. For - men. Be   hon-or   and be   glo-ry un-to   him.

Arranged by Ken Young

A - men.

Un - to the King   e - ter - nal,

un- to the King   im- mor- tal,   un- to the King   we lift our   praise.

35 We Bow Down

Psalm 95:6

Words and Music by
Twila Paris

1. You are Lord of cre-a - tion and Lord of my life, Lord of the land and the sea. You were Lord of the heav - ens be - fore there was time, and Lord of all lords you will be! We bow down and we wor - ship you, Lord. We bow down

2. You are King of cre-a - tion and King of my life, King of the land and the sea. You were King of the heav - ens be - fore there was time, and King of all kings you will be! We bow down and we crown you the King. We bow down

we bow down

Arranged by Ken Young

36 Hallelujah

Revelation 5:12

Words and Music by
Ken Young

Hal-le-lu - jah, Hal-le-lu - jah,
Hal-le-lu - jah, Hal-le-lu -
Hal-le-lu - jah,

Hal-le-lu - jah! Hal-le-lu - jah!
jah,

As we come to-ge-ther with a heart of praise for the

Lamb of Glo-ry and the An-cient of Days. May the Spir-it fill us with a

ho-ly ac-claim that re-stores God-ly pas-sion and re-moves world-ly shame.

A Simple Prayer

Adapted from the Prayer of St. Francis of Assisi
Matthew 10:39

Additional words by
Robin Lyle

(Men take lead) It is in giv - ing that we re - ceive, it is in par-

d'ning that we are par - doned. And it is in dy - ing that we are born

to e - ter - nal life. Make me an in-

stru - ment of your peace, I want to know what it's like to fol-

low you. When men look at me, I want them to see, the

light of the world in - side.

Arranged by Ken Young

38 The Joy of the Lord

Nehemiah 8:10

Words and Music by
Twila Paris

1. The joy of the Lord will be my strength;
2. The joy of the Lord will be my strength;
3. The joy of the Lord will be my strength;

I will not fal - ter, I will not faint.
He will up - hold me all of my days.
I will not waiv - er, walk - ing by faith.

He is my Sheph - erd, I am not a - fraid; the
I am sur - round - ed by mer - cy and grace; the
He will be strong to de - liv - er me safe; the

joy of the Lord is my strength.
joy of the Lord is my strength.
joy of the Lord is my strength. The

Arranged by Ken Young

joy of the Lord, the joy of the Lord, the

joy of the Lord is my strength. The joy of the Lord, the Lord,

joy of the Lord, the joy of the Lord is my strength.

39 Shine, Jesus, Shine

Words and Music by
Graham Kendrick

John 1:4-5

1. Lord, the light of your love is shin-ing, in the midst of the dark-ness shin-ing. Je-sus, light of the world, shine up-on us, set us free by the truth you now bring us.

2. Lord, I come to your awe-some pres-ence, from the shad-ows in-to your ra-diance. By the blood I may en-ter your bright-ness, search me, try me, con-sume all my dark - ness.

Shine on me, shine on me.

Shine, Je-sus, shine, fill this land with the Fa-ther's glo-ry.
Flow, riv-er, flow, flood the na-tions with grace and mer-cy.

Blaze, Spir-it, blaze, set our hearts on fire.
Send forth your Word, Lord, and let there be light.

Arranged by Ken Young

Wake Up, O Sleeper 40

Ephesians 5:8-20

Words and Music by
Ken Young

1. My God has said his light will shine; his light will shine in
2. The fruits of light his Spir - it gives are good - ness truth and

hearts of man. The fruit - less deeds of dark - ness past; re -
right - eous - ness. A new day breaks and all is clear; give

vealed by Christ with glo - rious hand. Wake
thanks to God, in Je - sus Christ.

up, O sleep - er, rise from the dead, and Christ will shine on you. Wake

up, O sleep - er, rise from the dead, and Christ will shine on you.

41 Hiding Place

Words and Music by
Steven Curtis Chapman & Jerry Salley

Psalm 32:6-7

1. In the dis - tance I can see the storm clouds
2. I'm not ask - ing you to take a - way my

com - ing my way, and I need to find a shel - ter be -
trou - bles Lord, 'cause it's thru the stor - my wea - ther I

fore it starts to rain. So I turn and run to you, Lord, you're the
learn to trust you more. So I thank you for your pro - mise,

on - ly place to go. Where un - fail - ing love sur - rounds me
I have come to know. Where un - fail - ing love sur - rounds me

when I need it most. You're my

Arranged by Ken Young

42 Higher Ground

Philippians 3:13-14

Words and Music by
Johnson Oatman & Chas. H. Gabriel

Arranged by Ken Young

43　　　　　　　Fellowship

Ecclesiastes 4:9-10

Words and Music by
Ken Young

1. We are peo - ple called to an un - com - mon pur - pose, a
2. When some - one cries there's a warm re - as - sur - ance, when

fam - 'ly forged by the nail - scarred hands.
some - one laughs there's an ech - o of cheer.

Stand - ing to - ge - ther on the Rock of A - ges;
Shar - ing to - ge - ther in a sweet com - mun - ion

bound to - ge - ther by the blood of the Lamb.
set be - fore us by a God who came near.

Fel - low - ship is the bond of be - liev - ers. Fel - low - ship is a
Fel - low - ship, Fel - low - ship,

three - strand - ed cord. Fel - low - ship is con - cern and com- pas-sion.
Fel - low - ship.

Fel - low - ship in the   name of the   Lord.

Lord.   Fel - low - ship in the   name of the   Lord.

44 Children of the Heavens

Matthew 19:14

Words and Music by
Ken Young

1. Ho-ly hands, touch us with your ten-der touch; re-
2. Ho-ly arms, keep us locked in your em-brace; pro-

move the web of fear that clouds our sight on things a-bove. And let us
tect us from the wick-ed-ness that hates your sav-ing grace. And let us

not for-get the rea-son that your son was cru-ci-fied; for you
keep our eyes on Je-sus and tell oth-ers there's a way to re-

want-ed us back home so bad you dared to let him die. We are
turn with him to heav-en when he comes that fi-nal day.

chil-dren of the heav-ens, once lost but now we're found; we're
heav-ens, once lost but now we're
but now we're found; we're

45 Glory

Words and Music by
Geoff Bullock

Psalm 24:9-10

Glo - ry to the King of kings.

Maj - es - ty, pow'r, and strength to the Lord of lords.

Glo - ry to the King of kings.
King

Maj - es - ty, pow'r, and strength to the Lord of lords.

1. Ho - ly One, all cre - a - tion crowns You, King of
2. Je - sus, Lord with eyes un - veiled, we will see Your
Ho - ly One, *crowns You* *King of*
Je - sus, *we will* *see Your*

kings. Ho - ly One, King of kings, Lord of
throne. Je - sus, Prince of Peace, Son of
kings. *Ho - ly One,* *King,*
throne. *Je - sus,* *Prince,*

Arranged by Ken Young

lords,   Ho - ly   One.
God,   Em - man - u   -   el.
Lord,   *Ho* - *ly*   *One.*
Son,   *Em* - *man* - *u* -   *el.*

Glo -   ry   to   the   King   of   kings.
                                            King

Maj - es - ty, pow'r, and strength to the Lord of lords. Pow'r, and

strength to the Lord   of   lords. Pow'r, and strength to the Lord   of lords.

46 Glorify the Lord With Me

Music by
Ken Young

Psalm 34:1-3

I will ex-tol the Lord at all times; His praise will al-ways be on my lips. My soul will boast in the Lord of all Lords; let the af-flict-ed hear and re-joice.

Glo-ri-fy the Lord with me; let us all ex-alt His name to-ge-ther. Glo-ri-fy the Lord with

Glo-ri-fy the Lord with me; let us all ex-alt His ho-ly name.

Glo-ri-fy the Lord with me; let us all ex-alt His ho-ly name.

Glo-ri-fy the Lord;

Step by Step

47

Psalm 63:1

Words and Music by
Beaker

O God, You are my God, and I will ev-er praise You.

I will seek You in the morn - ing, and I will learn to walk in Your

ways. And step by step You'll lead me, and I will

1. 2.

fol-low You all of my days. days. And I will fol-low You all of my

days, and I will fol-low You all of my days. And

step by step You'll lead me, and I will fol-low You all of my days.

Arranged by Ken Young

48 We Shall Assemble

Psalm 24:3-6

Words and Music by
Twila Paris

We shall as-sem-ble on the moun-tain, we shall as-sem-ble at the throne.

With hum-ble hearts in-to His pres-ence, we bring an of-fer-ing of song.

Glo-ry and hon-or and do - min - ion
Glo - ry and hon - or and do - ry

un - to the Lamb, un-to the King.
min - ion un-to the Lamb, un-to the

O, hal - le - lu - jah, hal - le - lu - jah!
King. O, hal - le - lu - jah!

We sing the song of the re - deemed.

Arranged by Ken Young

On Bended Knee

49

Psalm 95:6

Words and Music by
Robert Gay

On bend-ed knee I come, with a hum-ble heart I come,
On bend-ed knee we come, with a hum-ble heart we come,

bow-ing down be-fore Your ho-ly throne; Lift-ing
bow-ing down be-fore Your ho-ly throne; Lift-ing

ho-ly hands to You, as I pledge my love a-new, I
ho-ly hands to You, as we pledge our love a-new, we

wor-ship You in spir-it, I wor-ship You in truth. Make my
wor-ship You in spir-it, we wor-ship You in truth. Make our

1.

life a ho-ly praise un-to You.
lives a ho-ly praise un-to You.

2.

Make our lives a ho-ly praise un-to You.

Arranged by Ken Young

50   Blessed Be Your Name

Nehemiah 9:5-6, 32-34

Words and Music by
Ken Young

Bless - ed be Your name, / name,   your glo - ri - ous name;

may it be ex - alt - ed o - ver all names.

1. You a - lone are Lord   and you made the heav - ens,
2. You're a migh - ty God   and your deeds are awe - some,

all of the heav - ens and the star - ry host.
thru all our prob - lems your love en - dures.

You made the earth and all that is on it,
Noth - ing can hap - pen that your eye does not see it,

you made the seas from coast to coast.
All of the glo - ry and pow'r is yours.

You give life to all of the liv - ing, and the
Let us all re - mem - ber your warn - ings, Lord and

mul - ti - tudes in heav - en wor - ship you.
give us strength to o - bey your word.

D.C.

51 Listen to Our Hearts

Romans 8:26-27

Words and Music by
Jeff Moore & Steven Curtis Chapman

1. How do you ex-plain, how do you de-scribe
2. If words could fall like rain from these lips of mine,

a love that goes from east to west, and runs as deep as it is
and if I had a thou-sand years, Lord, I would still run out of

wide. You know all our hopes, Lord, you know all our
time. If you lis-ten to my heart, ev-'ry beat will

fears. And words can-not ex-press the love we feel
say, thank you for the life, thank you for the

but we long for you to hear.
truth, thank you for the way.

Arranged by Ken Young

52 Great Is the Lord Almighty

Exodus 14; Joshua 6

Words and Music by
Dennis Jernigan

The Lord reigns, he is a migh-ty God, the Lord God

reigns. reigns. Great is the Lord, Al - migh-ty he is

Lord, he is God in - deed. Great is the Lord, Al - migh-ty he is

God su-preme. Great is the Lord, Al - migh-ty he is

Lord, he is God in-deed. Great is the Lord. Great is the Lord.

Arranged by Ken Young

53 Glory of God

Genesis 1-3; Luke 9:28-36

Words and Music by
Ken Young

1. Cre - a - tion a - woke to the splen - dor of life, Je - ho - vah made man then He gave him a wife. To - geth - er they walked in the cool of the day, giv - ing praise to the glo - ry of God, as they

2. When ho - ly com - mun - ion was shat - tered by sin, and par - a - dise sud - den - ly came to an end, the wo - man fell down as they prayed, giv - ing praise to the glo - ry of God, as the

3. A man they called Je - sus knelt down as He prayed, know - ing that soon a great price must be paid, to tear down the cur - tain con - struct - ed by sin, that had hid - den the glo - ry of God, so the

1. giv - ing praise to the glo - ry of God.

each won-drous move that You make, as Your
each won-drous move that You made, how Your
glo - ry of God had come down, to the
1. watch-ing each won-drous move that You make.

pres - ence re - veals a mag - ni - fi - cent grace.
pres - ence re - vealed a mag - ni - fi - cent grace.
man and the wo - man who longed for His light.

Glo - ry of God, glo - ry of God, glo - ry of God, hal - le -

lu - jah! Let us once a - gain see the glo - ry of God,

Opt. modulation to key of D on 3rd verse.

glo - ry of God, hal - le - lu - jah! Glo - ry of God.

54 The Mystery of Godliness

1 Timothy 3:16

Music by
Ken Young

Deep Is Our Hunger for You 55

Matthew 5:6

Words and Music by
Michael James

1. Fa - ther, would you send your Spir - it to move thru your church once a - gain? Vis - it your peo - ple in pow-er, with heal - ing in your hand.

2. Fa - ther, would you send your Spir - it to rest on your chil - dren's heads? De- scend once a - gain on your cho- sen, O how we need to be fed.

Deep is our hun - ger for you, O how we yearn to be new. Loose, Lord, your Spir - it to come and re- new. Deep is our hun - ger for you.

Arranged by Ken Young

56 Revive Us, O Lord

Psalm 85:6

Words and Music by
Steve Camp & Carman Licciardello

1. We've turned from Your ways, Lord, Your fruit we've ceased to bear.
2. You have re-deemed us, in our dark-ness You sent light,

We lack the pow-er we once knew in our prayers.
to make us ho-ly and per-fect in Your sight.

That gen-tle voice from heav-en we
Tho' we've been un-faith-ful we've

cease to hear and know, the fact that He has
ne-ver been dis-owned, the Spir-it that raised

ris-en no long-er stirs our souls, (stirs our souls.)
Christ from the dead com-pells us to His throne, (to His throne.)

Arranged by Ken Young

Re - vive us, O Lord; re - vive us, O Lord, and cleanse us from our im - pur - i - ties, and make us ho - ly. Hear our cry, and re - vive us, O Lord.

57   At the Name of Jesus

Words and Music by
Dennis Jernigan

Philippians 2:9-11

At the name of Je-sus   ev'-ry knee will bow,   He is Lord, He is Lord.

At the name of Je-sus   ev'-ry tongue will shout,   He is Lord,   He is Lord.

He   is   Lord, He   is   Lord!   Bless-ed is the Ho-ly name,

(D.S.) You are   Lord, You   are   Lord!

bless-ed is the King who reigns,   bless-ed is the ho-ly name Je - sus.

Praise   Your   ho-ly   name.   Praise   Your   ho-ly   name.

Arranged by Ken Young

At the name of Je-sus ev'-ry knee will
At the name of Je-sus, ev'-ry knee will bow,

bow, You are Lord, You are Lord. At the name of
You are Lord, You are Lord. At the name of Je-sus

D.S.

Je-sus ev'-ry tongue will shout, You are Lord, You are Lord.
ev'-ry tongue will shout, You are Lord, You are Lord.

58   He Still Came

Words and Music by
Donna Douglas & Pam Thumb

Luke 2:4-7

1. No pal-ace, no jewels, no king-dom to rule, no crown of maj-es-
2. No fam'-ly, no friends, to help at the end, no out, no sub-sti-

ty. No throne and no robe, no sil-ver, no gold, no courts of roy-al-
tute. Much pain and much hurt, to give love and worth, He bore our sins and

ty. Yet the King of kings left heav-en to be-come a low-ly man. He
grief. Yet the hope of what He of-fered so out-weighed what must be done. He

left all heav-en's glo-ry to ful - fill His Fath-er's plan. He still
chose to be my vic-tor and as - sured my par-don won.

came, just for me He still came. Know-ing all He would en-dure, He still
He still came,

Arranged by Ken Young

came. Dis - re - gard - ing ev' - ry cost, from the man - ger to the cross, He still

came just for me, He still came. came.

Ho - ly, ho - ly, ho - ly! Lord God Al - migh - ty! Ear - ly in the

morn - ing our song shall rise to Thee. Ho - ly, ho - ly, ho - ly! Mer - ci - ful and

migh - ty! God in three per - sons, bless - ed Tri - ni - ty!

D.S. al Fine

59 Arise, My Love

Matthew 28:1-7

Words and Music by
Eddie Carswell

Expressive & freely

Ooh, Ooh, Ah, Ooh,

1. Not a word was heard at the tomb that day, just
2. Could it be that His Fa-ther had for - sak - en Him,

* Words to verses 3 & 4.

Ooh,
(Ah, on verse 4)

shuf- fling sol - diers' feet as they guard-ed the grave.
turned His back on His Son, de - spis - ing our sin.

Ooh,

One day, two days, three days had passed,
All hell seemed to whis - per, "Just for-get him, he's dead." Then the

Ooh,

Arranged by Ken Young

3. The earth trembled and the tomb began to shake,
And like lightening from heaven the stone rolled away;
And as dead men, the guards stood there in fright,
As the power of love displayed its might.

4. Then suddenly a melody filled the air,
Riding wings of wind, it was ev'rywhere;
The words all creation had been longing to hear,
The sweet sound of vict'ry, so loud and clear.

60 Rabboni

Words and Music by
Ken Young

John 20:10-16

1. You were there when the world had turned a- gainst me. When the
2. come once a- gain bring- ing all I have to of - fer, just to

dark- ness had pos- sessed my soul, Your ten- der mer - cy
find a dark and emp- ty tomb, Your ho- ly frame some-

made me whole. When I fol - lowed You, my
how ex - humed. Then I hear some- one say, "Why are

life was filled with mean - ing from the morn- ing to the ev'-
tears so free- ly fall - ing? Can't you hear the voice that's call-

2nd time to CODA

ning. I've seen the face of God.
ing? A voice that knows your name."

Bridge

When I close my eyes I can hear Your voice so clear- ly say - ing,
Ooh,

"Fa- ther, please for- give them for they know not what they do." What good
Ooh,

D.C. al CODA

rea- son did they have to do the things they did to You? So I

CODA - Refrain

"Rab- bo - ni! My Teach- er and my God! You're a-

live, and my bur- dens melt a - way. Rab- bo - ni! Sweet

Son of God Most High! I know death has lost its pow -

1.
2.

er and Your glo- ry's here to stay. stay.

61 Thomas' Song

John 20:24-29

Words and Music by
Ken Young

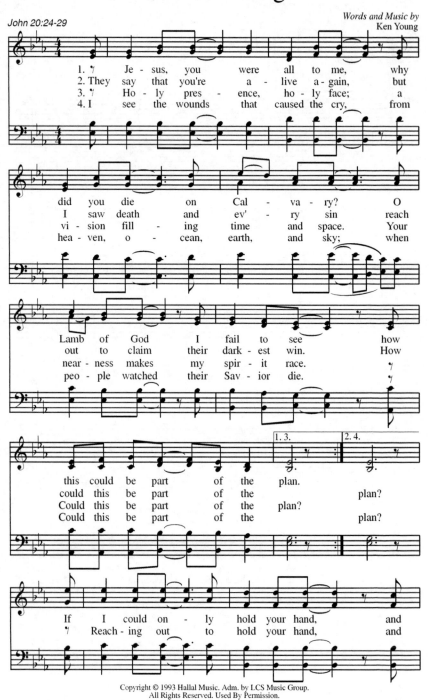

1. ⁊ Je - sus, you were all to me, why
2. They say that you're a - live a - gain, but
3. ⁊ Ho - ly pres - ence, ho - ly face; a
4. I see the wounds that caused the cry, from

did you die on Cal - va - ry? O
I saw death and ev' - ry sin reach
vi - sion fill - ing time and space. Your
hea - ven, o - cean, earth, and sky; when

Lamb of God I fail to see how
out to claim their dark - est win. How
near - ness makes my spir - it race. ⁊
peo - ple watched their Sav - ior die. ⁊

1. 3.
this could be part of the plan.
could this be part of the plan?
Could this be part of the plan?
Could this be part of the plan?

2. 4.

If I could on - ly hold your hand, and
⁊ Reach - ing out to hold your hand, and

touch the scars where nails were driv - en;
touch the scars where nails were driv - en;

I would need to feel your side where ho - ly flesh by
Com - ing near I feel your side where ho - ly flesh by

spear was riv - en. Then I'd be - lieve, on - ly
spear was riv - en. Now I be - lieve, Je - sus,

First time D.C., Second time to CODA

then I'd be - lieve your cru - el death was part of a heav - en - ly plan.
now I be - lieve your cru - el death was part of a heav - en - ly plan.

CODA

I proud - ly say with bla - zon cry, "You are my Lord and my God!"

62 How Beautiful

Isaiah 52:7

Words and Music by
Twila Paris

1. How beau-ti-ful the hands that served the wine and the bread, and the sons of the earth. How beau-ti-ful the feet that walked the long dust-y roads, and the hill to the cross.

2. How beau-ti-ful the ra-diant bride who waits for her groom with his light in her eyes. How beau-ti-ful when hum-ble hearts give the fruit of pure lives so that oth-ers may live.

3. How beau-ti-ful the feet that bring the sound of good news, and the love of the King. How beau-ti-ful the hands that serve the wine and the bread, and the sons of the earth.

How beau-ti-ful, how beau-ti-ful, how beau-ti-ful is the bo-dy of Christ.

1.

2. to Bridge
3. Fine

Christ.

Arranged by Ken Young

63 Come, Share the Lord

Matthew 26:26-28

Words and Music by
Bryan Jeffery Leech

1. We gath-er here in Je-sus' name, His love is burn-ing in our hearts like liv-ing flame. For through the lov-ing Son the Fa-ther makes us one. Come take the bread, come drink the wine, come share the Lord. No one is a strang-er here, ev-'ry one be-longs. Find-ing our for-give-ness here, we in turn for-give all wrongs.

2. He joins us here, He breaks the bread. The Lord who pours the cup is ris-en from the dead. The One we love the most is now our gra-cious host. Come take the bread, come drink the wine, come share the Lord. We are now a fam-i-ly of which the Lord is head. Though un-seen He meets us here in the break-ing of the bread.

3. We'll gath-er soon where an-gels sing. We'll see the glo-ry of our Lord and com-ing King. Now we an-ti-ci-pate the feast for which we wait. Come take the bread, come drink the wine, come share the Lord.

D.C.

Arranged by Ken Young

Breath of Heaven

64

John 20:22

Words and Music by
Chris Eaton & Amy Grant

Breath of Heav-en, hold me to-ge-ther, be for-ev-er near me, Breath of Heav-en. Breath of Heav-en, light-en my dark-ness, pour o-ver me Your ho-li-ness, for You are ho-ly.

1. You, and You a-lone are ho-ly.

rit.

2. ho-ly. Breath of Heav-en, Breath of Breath of Heav-en,

Heav-en, Breath of Heav-en, Heav-en. Breath of Heav-en, Breath of Heav-en.

Arranged by Ken Young

65 Blessed Jesus

Philippians 4:6-7

Words and Music by
Joey Holder

Arranged by Pam Stephenson

66   Lord, I Lift Your Name on High

Revelation 15:3-4

Words and Music by
Rick Founds

Arranged by Ken Young

67 Peace

John 16:33

Words and Music by
Sy Gorieb & Tim Hosman

1. I will wor-ship the Lord, for He is wor-thy;
2. Feel the pres-ence of God up-on the wa-ter;

(wor - thy) I will lay down my sword, the Prince of
(wa - ter) Hear the voice of the Lord with-in the

Peace is His name. King of the flood, the Lord is
thun-der that rolls. King of the flood, the Lord is

migh-ty; (migh-ty) The Lord can quench the e - vil
migh-ty; (migh-ty) The Lord can calm the trou-bled

flame, the e - vil flame. Peace when trou - ble
soul, trou-u - bled soul. Peace when sor - row

Arranged by Ken Young

68 Faithful Love

Words and Music by
Ken Young

Psalm 89:1

1. Faith-ful love flow-ing down from the thorn-cov-ered crown, makes me whole, saves my soul, wash-es whit-er than snow. Faith-ful love calms each fear, reach-es down, dries each tear; holds my hand when I can't stand on my own. Faith-ful love from a - bove came to

2. Faith-ful love is a friend just when hope seems to end, wel-come face, sweet em-brace, ten-der touch filled with grace. Faith-ful love, end-less pow'r, liv-ing flame, Spir-it's fire; burn-ing bright in the night, guid-ing my way.

Faith-ful love, from a - bove

earth to show the Fa - ther's love. And I'll

nev - er be the same, for I've
And I'll nev - er be the same,

seen faith - ful love face to face, and Je - sus is his

1. name.

2. name.

69 Jubilee

Words and Music by
Michael Card

Leviticus 25

1. The Lord pro - vid - ed for a time for the slaves
2. At the Lord's ap - point-ed time His deep de - sire

to be set free; For the debts to all be can - celled so His
be - came a man; The heart of all true ju - bi - la - tion, and with

cho - sen ones could see. His deep de - sire
joy we un - der-stand. In His voice

was for for - give - ness, He longed to see
we hear a trum - pet sound that tells

their lib - er - ty; And His yearn-ing was em - bod - ied in the
us we are free. He is the in - car - na - tion of the

Arranged by Ken Young

70 Thank You, Lord

2 Corinthians 9:15

Words and Music by
Dennis L. Jernigan

For all that You've done, I will thank You, for all that You're going to do. For all that You've prom-ised, and all that You are is all that has car-ried me through, Je-sus, I thank You!

And I thank You, thank You, Lord. And I
And I thank You, thank You, Lord. And I

Lord. And I thank You, thank You.
thank You, thank You Lord.

Arranged by Ken Young

Copyright © 1990 Shepherd's Heart Music.
All Rights Reserved. Used By Permission.

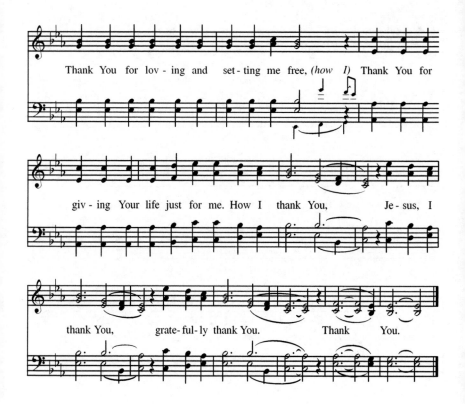

Thank You for lov - ing and set - ting me free, *(how I)* Thank You for giv - ing Your life just for me. How I thank You, Je - sus, I thank You, grate-ful- ly thank You. Thank You.

71   Give Thanks

Colossians 2:6-7

Words and Music by
Henry Smith

Give thanks with a grate-ful heart, give thanks to the Ho-ly One; Give thanks be-cause He's giv-en Je-sus Christ, His Son. Give thanks with a grate-ful heart, give thanks to the Ho-ly One; Give thanks be-cause He's giv-en Je-sus Christ, His Son. His on-ly Son. And now let the

weak say, "I am strong," let the poor say, "I am rich," be-cause of
sick say, "I am whole," let the bound say, "I am free," be-cause of

Arranged by Ken Young

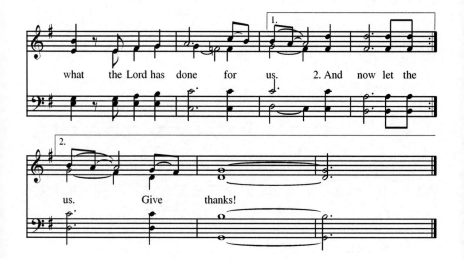

what   the Lord has done   for   us.   2. And now let the

us.   Give   thanks!

72 Worthy Is the Lamb

Words to "Just As I Am" by Charlotte Elliott
Music by Wm. Bradbury

Revelation 5

1. O ho - ly Lamb, thou Son of God; Most
2. You a - lone are wor - thy to o - pen its seals, be -

ho - ly Lord, most wor - thy Lord. Stand - ing in the cen - ter
cause You were slain and gave Your blood. You pur - chased ev' - ry

of God's throne, O wor - thy is the Lamb, the Lamb.
man for God, O wor - thy is the Lamb, the

1.

2.

Lamb. Ooh,

You re - ceive all pow - er and wis - dom and strength, be

Arranged by Ken Young
Words to verses 1-3 by Jeff Nelson

Son of His Love

73

Matthew 3:16-17

Words and Music by
Ken Young

Baritone lead

Je - sus, Re - deem - er, Mes - si - ah, Ya - shu - a, the

His love

Lamb of His glo - ry, the Son of His love.

Je - sus, Re - deem - er, Mes - si - ah, Ya - shu - a,

Je - sus, Re - deem - er, Mes - si - ah, Ya - shu - a, the

Lamb of His glo - ry, Son of His love.

Lamb of His glo - ry, the Son of His love.

74   O Sacred Head

Matthew 27:27-31

Bernard of Clairvaux, Tr. J.W. Alexander
Hans L. Hassler, 16th Cent.

Arranged by Ken Young

75   For the Sake of the Call

Matthew 4:18-22

Words and Music by
Steven Curtis Chapman

1. No - bo - dy stood and ap - plaud - ed them, so they
2. nets ly - ing there at the wa - ter's edge, told a
3. Drawn like the ri - vers are drawn to the sea; There's

knew from the start this road would not lead to
sto - ry that few could be - lieve and none could ex -
no turn - ing back, for the wa - ter can - not help but

fame. All they real - ly knew for sure was Je - sus had
plain; How some cra - zy fish - er - men a - greed to go
flow. Once we hear the Sav - ior's call we'll fol - low where-

called to them, He said, "Come fol - low me" and they
where Je - sus led, with no thought for what they might
ev - er He leads, be - cause of the love He has

1.
came, with reck - less a - ban - don they came. 2. Emp - ty
gain, for
shown, be -

Arranged by Ken Young

2. 3.

Je - sus had called them by name. And they an - swered,
cause He has called us to go. We will an - swer,

"We will a - ban - don it all, for the

sake of the call; No o - ther rea - son at all, but the

sake of the call. Whol - ly de - vo - ted to

live and to die, for the sake of the call."

76 We Will Serve the Lord

Joshua 24:15

Words and Music by
Ken Young

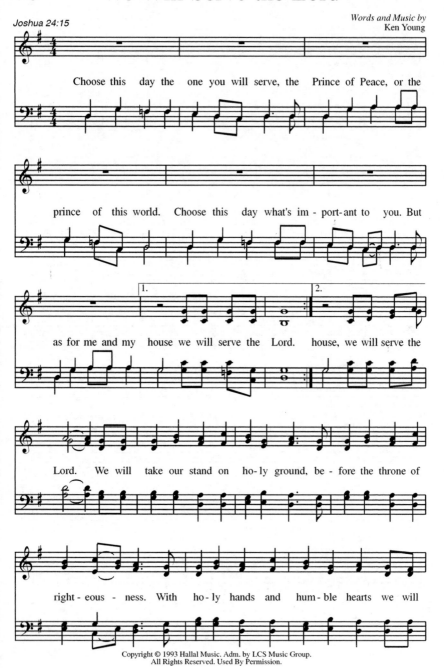

Choose this day the one you will serve, the Prince of Peace, or the prince of this world. Choose this day what's im - port-ant to you. But as for me and my house we will serve the Lord. house, we will serve the Lord. We will take our stand on ho - ly ground, be - fore the throne of right - eous - ness. With ho - ly hands and hum - ble hearts we will

serve the King of Kings.__ We will serve the King of Kings.

Choose this day the one you will serve, the Prince of Peace, or the

prince of this world. Choose this day what's im - port - ant to you. But

as for me and my house, we will serve the Lord. But

as for me and my house, we will serve the Lord.

77 Broken Things

Romans 8:28

Words and Music by
Ken Young

1. My fa - ther's fa - ther worked this land, for ma - ny
years I took my stand. But the plow is heav - y and I can't hold
on to the le - ga - cy of the farm - er's song.

2. I'll re - mem - ber the days with the sun on the
3. Give me what I need, not what I de -

Ooh,
Need, de -

land, wip - ing sweat from my brow with a rough cal - loused
mand. Send me heav - en - filled hopes, not earth - made

Ooh,
mand. Hopes,

things,   who thru bro-ken clouds   gives us sweet, sweet

us - es bro-ken things,   who thru bro-ken clouds   gives us

things,   who thru bro-ken clouds   gives us sweet, sweet

rain.   Who   gives   us   bread   from   bro - ken

rain.   Who   gives   us   bread   from

rain.   Who   gives   us   bread   from   bro - ken

grain.   O, Lord make me strong-er   thru bro-ken   things.

bro - ken grain.   Lord make me strong-er   thru bro-ken   things.

grain.   O, Lord make me

78 We Believe In God

Words and Music by
Amy Grant & Wes King

2 Timothy 1:12

Arranged by Ken Young

don't be a - fraid to show it. 2. If
all in this place will know it.

We be - lieve in God, and we
God, yes, we be - lieve and

all need Je - sus. sus.
we

79   You Are My All in All

2 Corinthians 12:10

Words and Music by
Dennis L. Jernigan

PART I

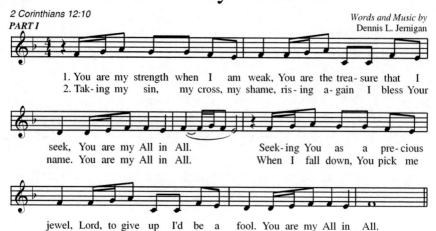

1. You are my strength when I am weak, You are the trea-sure that I
2. Tak-ing my sin, my cross, my shame, ris-ing a-gain I bless Your

seek, You are my All in All.   Seek-ing You as a pre-cious
name. You are my All in All.   When I fall down, You pick me

jewel, Lord, to give up I'd be a fool. You are my All in All.
up; When I am dry, You fill my cup. You are my All in All.

PART II

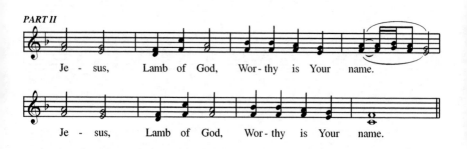

Je - sus, Lamb of God, Wor-thy is Your name.

Je - sus, Lamb of God, Wor-thy is Your name.

CHORUS

Je- sus, Lamb of God, Wor-thy is Your name.

Arranged by Ken Young

3

Je - sus,   Lamb of   God,   Wor- thy is Your name.

Wor - thy   is   Your   name.

All sing in unison on vs. 1
Women sing Part II, men sing vs. 2
Men sing Part II, women sing vs. 1
All sing Chorus

80 Thank You for Mothers

Ephesians 6:2-3

Words and Music by
Ken Young

1. Lord, in Your wis-dom You gave us some-one,
2. Lord, through Your mer-cy You gave us some-one,

1. some-one to hold us through the long, lone-ly nights. Some-one to
2. some-one to no-tice ev-'ry tear that was cried. Some-one to

1. laugh at the sil-li-est things, some-one to lov-ing-ly
2. mag-ic-'ly make things al-right, some-one to read us sweet

1. call out our names. But, most of all Fa-ther, we thank You for
2. sto-ries at night.

moth-ers who pray for their chil-dren ev-'ry day.

People Need the Lord

81

Psalm 40:17

Words and Music by
Greg Nelson & Phil McHugh

Peo - ple need the Lord, peo - ple need the Lord.

At the end of bro - ken dreams He's the o - pen door.

Peo - ple need the Lord, peo - ple need the Lord. When will we

re - al - ize that peo - ple need the Lord. Lord.

Arranged by Tom Fettke

82 Instruments of Your Peace

Words and Music by
Kirk & Deby Dearman

Matthew 5:9

Lord, make us in - stru - ments of Your peace;

Where there is ha - tred let Your love in - crease.

Lord, make us in - stru - ments of Your peace;

Walls of pride and prej - u - dice shall cease,

Fine

when we are Your in - stru - ments of peace.

1. Where there is ha - tred, we will sow Your love;
2. Where there is blind - ness, we will pray for sight;

Ooh,

83   Love One Another

John 13:34,35

Music by
Ken Young

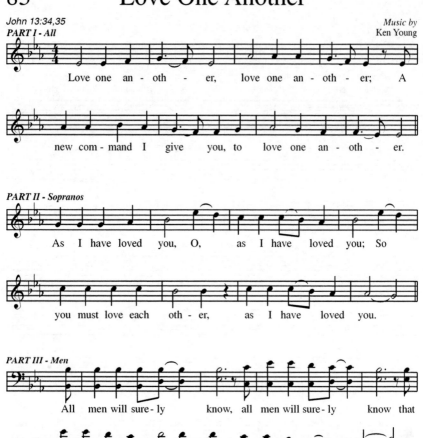

PART I - All

Love one an - oth - er, love one an - oth - er; A

new com - mand I give you, to love one an - oth - er.

PART II - Sopranos

As I have loved you, O, as I have loved you; So

you must love each oth - er, as I have loved you.

PART III - Men

All men will sure-ly know, all men will sure-ly know that

you are my dis - ci - ples, all men will sure-ly know.

Restore My Soul

84

Psalm 23:3

Words and Music by
Sylvia Rose

1. Re-store my spir-it, Lord, I need re-stored; *(Lord, you know that)*
2. Re-vive the fi-re, Lord, deep in my soul; *(Won't you, Lord)*
3. Re-new my cour-age, Lord, it needs re-stored; *(Yes, it does, for)*

My heart is wear-y, please help me, dear Lord.
Stir my de-si-re to work in Your fold.
my cup is emp-ty, re-fill it, dear Lord.

I stand in need of more strength from Your Word. Re-
Light in my heart, dear God, Your zeal grown cold. Re-
Re-place all doubts and fear with faith so bold. Re-

Re-

new my love, re-build my faith, Oh, re-store my soul.
new my love, re-build my faith, Oh, re-store my soul.
new my love, re-build my faith, Oh, re-store my soul.

new, re-build,

Arranged by Ken Young

85   I Stand in Awe

Psalm 33:8

Words and Music by
Mark Atrogge

You are beau-ti-ful be-yond de-scrip-tion, too mar-vel-ous for words,

Too won-der-ful for com - pre-hen - sion, like noth-ing ev-er seen or heard.

Who can grasp Your in-fi-nite wis-dom, who can fath-om the depth of Your love?

You are beau-ti-ful be-yond de - scrip-tion, maj-es - ty en-throned a-bove.

Refrain

And I stand, I stand in awe of You, I stand, I stand in awe of You;

Ho-ly God, to whom all praise is due, I stand in awe of You. You.

Arranged by Reid Lancaster

I Exalt Thee

86

Psalm 97:9

Words and Music by
Pete Sanchez, Jr.

For Thou, O Lord, art high a-bove all the earth. Thou art ex-

alt-ed far a-bove all gods. bove all gods.

Descant on last refrain

I ex - alt Thee, I ex - alt Thee.

Refrain

I ex-alt Thee, I ex - alt Thee, I ex-

alt Thee, O Lord. O Lord.

Opt. ending for refrain repeat

O Lord.

87 Hosanna

Words and Music by
Greg Nelson & Phil McHugh

Mark 11:9

1. Ho - san - na, Ho - san - na, Ho - san - na in the high -
2. Wor - thy, Wor - thy, Wor - thy is the King of

Refrain

est; est; Lord, we lift up Your name,
kings; kings; Lord, we lift up Your name, With

With hearts full of praise; Be ex - alt - ed, O
hearts full, hearts full of praise; So be ex - alt - ed, O

Lord, my God, Ho - san - na in the high - est.

Arranged by Reid Lancaster

Holy Is the Lord

Psalm 99:5

Words and Music by
Steve Holcomb

Arranged by Tom Fettke and Bill Wolaver

89 So Worthy

Words and Music by
Ken Young

Revelation 5:12

1. Wor - thy, so wor - thy, is the Son who came to earth and left all his glo - ry. See His ma - je - sty, O what a mys - ter - y; Just to think that One so in - cre - di - bly mar - ve - lous came for me. He's so

2. wor - thy, so wor - thy, with such grace He faced a storm of ha - tred and en - mi - ty. See His

3. Wor - thy, so wor - thy, is the Son who lives a - gain, what glor - i - ous vic - to - ry. See His

what mys - ter - y;

90 Every Knee Shall Bow

Words and Music by
Twila Paris

Philippians 2:10

1. As the sun ris - es in the east, He shall split the east-ern
2. Come the dawn of the Prince of Peace, like the morn-ing af - ter

sky. Sword in hand up-on the moun - tain, fire of heav-en in His
rain. There shall be no more of ha - tred, nei-ther sor-row, nei-ther

Refrain

eyes. And ev-'ry knee shall bow, ev'ry knee shall
pain. Ev-'ry knee shall bow,

bow. We kneel be - fore Him
ev - 'ry knee shall bow.

now, and ev-'ry knee shall bow. bow.
kneel be - fore Him now, We

Arranged by Ken Young

Purify My Heart

91

Words and Music by
Jeff Nelson

Isaiah 6:6,7

Pur - i - fy my heart, touch me with Your cleans-ing fi - re. Take me to the cross, Your ho - li - ness is my de - si - re. Breathe Your life in me, kin - dle the love that flows from Your throne. Oh, pur - i - fy my heart, pur - i - fy my heart.

Arranged by Ken Young

92 He Is the God

Ho - ly One? The proud bow down be - fore His feet!

3. His won-ders great are fa-thomed not; His mir - a- cles are

count- ed not. He pass-es by with hid - den hand; He

is the God, the God of man. He is the God, the God of man.

93   A Mighty Fortress

Psalm 18:2

Words & Music by
Martin Luther

A migh - ty for - tress is our God,   a
Our help - er He,   a - mid   the flood   of

1.

bul - wark nev - er fail - ing;
mor - tal ills pre - vail - ing.

2.

For still our an - cient foe doth seek to work us

woe; His craft and pow'r are great, and armed with

cru - el hate, on earth is not his e - qual.

A migh-ty for - tress is our God, a bul-wark nev - er fail - ing;

To CODA on last pass

Our help- er He, a - mid the flood of mor- tal ills pre - vail - ing.

Arranged by Ken Young

94 Still Listening

Words and Music by
Steven Curtis Chapman & Geoff Moore

Psalm 145:18,19

1. I would lay me down to sleep, pray the Lord my
2. Years can take us far a - way from the sim - ple
3. I will nev - er un - der-stand how the words of

soul to keep. And though I nev - er
child - like faith. But I am long - ing
mor - tal man can reach the ears of

saw Him there, I be - lieve He heard each prayer.
to re - turn, to the place where I first learned
One so pure and touch His heart, but they do I'm sure.

For God was great and God was good, and I knew if I spoke the words,
that God is great and God is good, so I will speak the words:
For God is great and God is good, and he is love.

He would be list - en - ing.

Arranged by Ken Young

God our Fa - ther, once a - gain I bow my head to pray.

You are my Fa - ther and my friend, and You hear ev - 'ry word I

say. A prayer for for - give - ness, a
Ooh,

des - perate cry for help, or praise flow-ing from a thank - ful heart. Like
Ah,

D.S. (vs.1) al Fine on last pass

each time be - fore I come know-ing Your still list-en-ing.

95 Rise Up, O Men of God

Words and Music by
William Merrill, William Walter,
Bill Batstone, and Buddy Owens

Ephesians 6:10

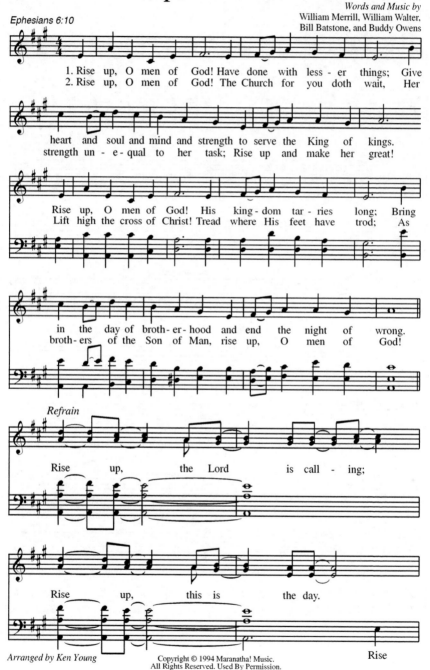

1. Rise up, O men of God! Have done with less-er things; Give
2. Rise up, O men of God! The Church for you doth wait, Her

heart and soul and mind and strength to serve the King of kings.
strength un-e-qual to her task; Rise up and make her great!

Rise up, O men of God! His king-dom tar-ries long; Bring
Lift high the cross of Christ! Tread where His feet have trod; As

in the day of broth-er-hood and end the night of wrong.
broth-ers of the Son of Man, rise up, O men of God!

Refrain

Rise up, the Lord is call-ing;

Rise up, this is the day.

Rise

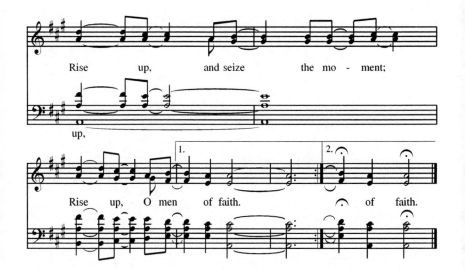

Rise up, and seize the mo - ment;
up,

Rise up, O men of faith. of faith.

96 The Battle Belongs to the Lord

Isaiah 54:17

Words and Music by
Jamie Owens-Collins

1. In heav-en-ly ar-mor we'll en-ter the land, the
2. When the pow-er of dark-ness comes in like a flood, the
3. When your en-e-my press-es in hard, do not fear, the

bat-tle be-longs to the Lord. No wea-pon that's fash-ioned a-gainst
bat-tle be-longs to the Lord. He's raised up a stand-ard, the pow'r
bat-tle be-longs to the Lord. Take cour-age, my friend, your re-demp-

us will stand, the bat-tle be-longs to the Lord.
of His blood, the bat-tle be-longs to the Lord.
tion is near, the bat-tle be-longs to the Lord.

Refrain

And we sing glo-ry, hon-or, pow-er and strength to the Lord.

We sing glo-ry, hon-or, pow-er and strength to the Lord.

Arranged by Reid Lancaster

97 Heal This Land

Words and Music by
Ken Young

2 Chronicles 7:13,14

When the heav-ens cease to rain their bless-ings on this na-tion;

When the land is con-sumed, and the sin o-ver-takes us.

When the dark-ness falls up-on us, when the light no long-er shines,
When the dark-ness falls up-on us, when the light no long-er shines.

Sure-ly then, bro-ken-heart-ed, we will stop and hear this cry:

"If my peo-ple, my dear child-ren, who are called by my name,
who are called by my

Will bow low in my pre-sence, turn a-gain, seek my face;
turn a - gain, and seek my face;

Then will I hear from heav - en, reach-ing down will take their
I will hear from heav - en, reach-ing down will take their,

hand. Bring new hope for this na - tion, bring a heal-ing to this
take their hand.

1. land." Bring new
2. land." Re - new our hearts, and heal this land!

98 I Pledge Allegiance to the Lamb

1 Peter 4:12,13

Words and Music by
Ray Boltz

I pledge al-le-giance to the Lamb, with all my strength, with all I am. I will seek to ho-nor his com-mands, I pledge al-le-giance to the Lamb, to the Lamb.

I have heard how Christ-ians ⁊ long a-go ⁊ were
Now the years have come, ⁊ the years have gone, and the

Ooh,

Arranged by Ken Young

one by one they chose to die, the
one by one let us live our lives, for the

One by one they chose to die.
One by one we'll live our lives.

Son of God they would not de - ny. Like a
One who died to give us life. Till the

Ooh,

great an - gel - ic choir sings, I can
trum - pet sounds on that fi - nal day, let us

Great an - gel - ic cho - ir sings.
Trum - pet sounds that fi - nal day.

99 Rushing Wind

Hebrews 12:28,29

Words and Music by
Dennis L. Jernigan

PART I

1. Rush - ing Wind, blow through me with your ten - der breeze!
2. There is no friend to me like you long to be,
3. There is no one like you that I've ev - er known, who

Search out the depths of my heart! Like a
down here be - low or a - bove! Rush - ing
sings me a love song like you! Let your

Fire, burn through me here on my knees! Con -
Wind, help me see my Fa - ther and be a
Wind blow right through! My heart is your home, and

sume ev - 'ry dark hid - den part!
ves - sel of his ten - der love!
I am here wait - ing for you!

PART II

Ho - ly Spir - it! All con - sum - ing Fire!

Fill me! Fill me with the joy of my heart's de - sire!

Refrain

Ho - ly Spir - it! All con - sum - ing Fire!

Arranged by Ken Young

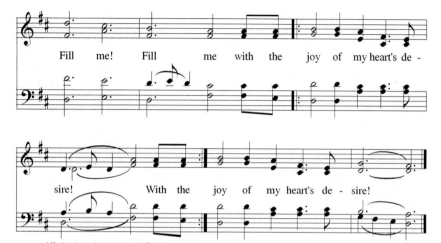

Fill me! Fill me with the joy of my heart's de-

sire! With the joy of my heart's de-sire!

All sing in unison on vs. 1, Part 1
Men sing vs. 2, Part 1 - Women sing Part 2
Women sing vs. 3, Part 1 - Men sing Part 2
All sing Refrain

My Yoke Is Easy

100

Matthew 11:28,29

Words and Music by
Dennis L. Jernigan

1. Did you think that there would nev-er be a way?
That the sea of sin would fi-n'lly sweep you much too far a-way?
Did you think that soon the load you car-ry you could just not bear? Did you real-ly think that no one real-ly cares?
Come to Me all who are wear-y, search-ing for life's best.

Arranged by Ken Young

Take My yoke of love up-on you and come in-to My rest.

Refrain

For My yoke is eas - y,

For My yoke is eas - y, and My

and My bur-den is light. How I've

bur-den is light. and My bur-den is light.

al-ways longed to car - ry you through the end - less night.

For My yoke is eas - y,

For My yoke is eas - y, and My

101 In the Lord Alone

Ephesians 3:14-18

Words and Music by
Walt Harrah

1. In the Lord, the Lord a-lone are right-eous-ness and strength. The
2. In the Lord, the Lord a-lone are life and health and peace. His
3. In the Lord, the Lord a-lone is ev'-ry-thing I need. The

height and breadth and length of love is found in Him.
mer-cies and His lov-ing kind-ness ne-ver cease.
Son of Man now reign-ing high will int-er-cede.

In the Lord, the Lord a-lone are right-eous-ness andstrength.
In the Lord, the Lord a-lone are life and health and peace.
In the Lord, the Lord a-lone is ev'-ry-thing I need.

In the Lord, in the Lord a-lone.

Arranged by Ken Young

Optional solo for vs. 2

102 Enter In

Acts 7:54-56

Words and Music by
Ken Young

1. In a world of pain and sor-row, where the
2. When the dreams of life are shat-tered, and the

sor - row,
shat - tered,

best so oft-en fall. When the prayers all go un-
bo-dy wastes a-way. When all dig-ni-ty's a-
the best so of-ten fall.
the bo-dy wastes a-way.

ans - wered, when the sha-dows seem to ov-er-whelm, when the
ban - doned, and the ones who care, with bro-ken hearts, plead for
ans - wered, sha - dows ov-er-whelm,
ban - doned, ones with bro-ken hearts,

light of hope has dimmed and leaves no hope at all.
mer-cy, but it seems that Mer - cy hides His face.

Refrain

That's when heav-en pierc-es through the cloud of dark-ness, and the
heav - en

103 Much Grace Was On Them All

Words and Music by
Ken Young

Acts 4:31-35

1. They all came to-ge - ther with one heart and with one mind;
2. They took their pos-ses - sions, and they said, "These are just things.

they shared with each oth - er, no not one was left be - hind.
Let us sell our hous - es, pre - cious jewels, and dia - mond rings.

With great pow'r the mes - sage giv - en by the
For our bro - thers and our sis - ters some - times

ones who heard the call; told of Je - sus' re - sur - rec -
stum - ble, some - times fall, from the hung - er - ing and thirst-

tion, and much grace was on them all. Yes, much
ing, and this grace is for us all."

Optional Ending: Repeat chorus, modulating up to Ab. Close with a repeat of:
"And they overflowed with love - Yes, they overflowed with love - Let us overflow...with love."

104   We Welcome You

Romans 12:10,11

Words and Music by
Ken Young

We wel-come you to our fam-i-ly, and we
hand in hand we will serve the Lord, and to-

hope you find the light of Je-sus shin-ing in this place. Walk-ing
ge-ther we will ce-le-brate His

mer-cy and His grace. This is home for the lone-ly, to the tired

a place of rest. It's a house of de-vo-tion to the Dear - est and the

Best. We wel-come you to our fam-i-ly, and we

hope you find the light of Je-sus shin-ing in this place.

105 Holy, Holy, Holy Lord

Matthew 21:9

Words and Music by
Peter Scholtes

Arranged by Reid Lancaster

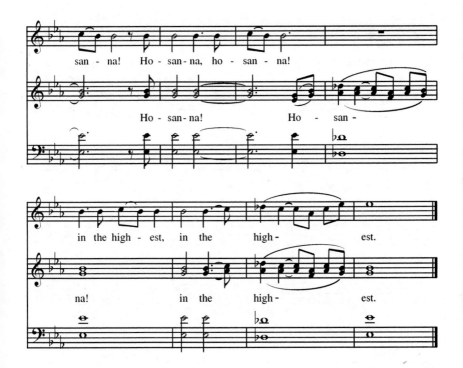

106   Highest Place

Words and Music by
Ramon Pink

Hebrews 4:14

We place You on the high-est place, for You are the great High
Priest. We place You high a-bove all else, all
else; And we come to You and wor-ship at Your feet.

We place You on the high-est place,
We place You on the high-est place, for
for You are the great High Priest.
You are the great High Priest. We place

Cresc.

Arranged by Pam Stephenson

We place You high a - bove all   else,   all   else.
You
And   we   come to You and   wor- ship at Your   feet.

107   Great Are You Lord

Psalm 48:1

Words and Music by
Steve & Vikki Cook

Ho - ly Lord, most Ho - ly Lord, You a - lone are wor - thy
of my praise; O Ho - ly Lord, most Ho - ly Lord, with
all of my heart I sing.
              sing, with my heart I sing.

Great are You, Lord, great are You,
            great are you, Lord,

wor - thy of praise; Ho - ly and
Lord, wor - thy of praise. Ho - ly and true,
            and so ho - ly,

true, great are You, Lord, most Ho - ly Lord.
ho - ly and true, great are You

Arranged by Ken Young

108   Richly Blest

Philippians 4:10-13

Words and Music by
Ken Young

1. Blu-est sky, cloud-y day, wheth-er it's good or bad that tends to come my way. From the high-est hill or deep-est val-ley I will claim His rest, for the One who loves me makes me rich-ly blest.

2. Fresh de-light, deep la-ment, wheth-er in joy or pain I've learned to be con-tent. For the One who fills me with His Spir-it al-ways knows what's best, and the

blest. And I know that life is like a ship that sails out on the sea, some-times
sails, sails out on the

To CODA on last pass

cra-dled by the calm, and some-times plunged in-to the fu-ry. But a
sea, and some-times plunged in-to the

peace with-in my heart pro-vides a warm and sweet car-ess, for the
fu-ry.

D.C. al Fine

One who loves me makes me rich-ly blest.

One who loves me makes me rich-ly blest. For the

Fine

One who loves me makes me rich-ly blest.

109 The Light of Life

John 8:12

Words and Music by
Sy Gorieb & Nick Riso

1. Dark-ness a-waits the dawn, morn-ing a-wakes cre-
2. Ev - 'ry day peo - ple pray they'll find the strength to
a - waits the dawn,
yes, peo - ple pray

a - tion's song. And with the ris - ing sun,
make it through. While there is One who waits
the ris - ing sun,
One who still waits

hope comes a - live to car - ry on.
to fill their hearts with life a - new.

Descant

Shin - ing on, o -

The light of life is shin-ing on, the dark of night can't

Arranged by Ken Young

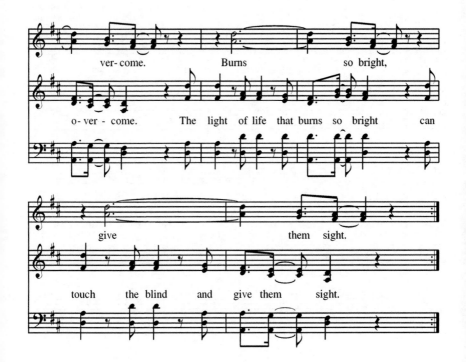

110 And Can It Be

Words and Music by
Charles Wesley & Bob Kauflin

Romans 5:8

1. And can it be that I should gain an int - 'rest in my Sav - ior's blood? Died He for me, who caused His pain? For me, who scorned His per - fect love. A - maz - ing love! How can it be that You, my God, would die for me. A - maz - ing love! How

2. You left Your Fa - ther's throne a - bove, so free and in - fi - nite Your grace. Emp - tied Your - self of all but love, and bled for A - dam's help - less race.

3. Bold - ly I come be - fore Your throne to claim Your mer - cy im - mense and free. No great - er love will e'er be known, for O my God it found out me.

Arranged by Ken Young

111 My Eyes Are Dry

Psalm 51:1,2

Words and Music
Keith Green

My eyes are dry, my faith is old, my heart is hard, my prayers are cold. And I know how I ought to be, a - live to You and dead to me. What can be done to an old heart like mine? Soft - en it up with oil and wine. The oil is You, Your Spir - it of love. Please wash me a - new in the wine of Your blood.

112 When I Fell in Love With You

Matthew 22:37

Words and Music by
Dennis Jernigan

1. When I fell in love with You, I fell hard. What else could I do? You took the old and left me new. When I fell in love with You.

2. My heart broken, all hope lost, Cold and hard, rav-aged, wound-ed tossed. I heard Your love song from the cross. Then I fell in love with You. When I fell in love with You,

3. Sin had bound me through and through, with ev-'ry fail-ure the dark-ness grew. Your love fell down with crim-son hue. Then I gave my heart to You.

4. You were wait-ing, Your love true, me, de-bat-ing just what to do. My heart was healed when You broke through. Then I fell in love with You.

love with You, You swept me off my feet. swept me off my

Arranged by Ken Young

113 Light the Fire

Words and Music by
Jo Ann Maxwell

Luke 24:32

1. I stand to praise You, but I fall to my
2. I feel Your arms a-round me, as the pow'r of Your heal-ing be-

knees. My spir-it is will-ing, but my flesh is so
gins. Your spir-it moves right thru me, like a migh-ty rush-ing

weak. Light the fire, in my soul; fan the flame,
wind. Light the fire, in my wear-y

make me whole. Lord, You know where I've
soul; fan the flame, make my spir-it whole. Lord, You know

been; so light the fire in my heart a-gain.
where I've been

Arranged by Brandon Thomas & Ken Young

Romans 12:1

Unknown

My heart, my mind, my bod-y, my soul I give to You, take con-trol. I give my bod-y a liv-ing sac-ri-fice. Lord, take con-trol, take con-trol.

*Lord, I am serious about
living this new life with You.
My heart, my mind, my body
and my soul are Yours.
Take control, Lord.
I surrender everything to You:
the words of my mouth,
the meditation of my heart,
all that I own, all that I am.
Fill me with compassion,
kindness, humility,
quiet strength, and discipline.
Make me a living sacrifice,
Lord, take control.*

115   Stream In the Desert

Words and Music by
Ken Young

Isaiah 35:1-6

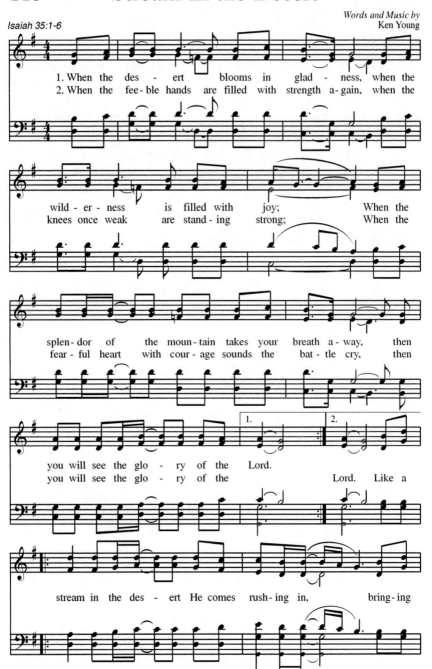

1. When the des - ert blooms in glad - ness, when the
2. When the fee - ble hands are filled with strength a - gain, when the

wild - er - ness   is filled with   joy;   When the
knees once weak   are stand - ing   strong;   When the

splen - dor   of   the moun - tain takes your   breath a - way,   then
fear - ful heart   with cour - age sounds the   bat - tle cry,   then

1.
you will see the glo - ry of the   Lord.

2.
you will see the glo - ry of the   Lord.   Like a

stream in the des - ert He comes rush - ing in,   bring - ing

life to the burn - ing des - ert sand. Then the

blind see, the deaf hear, the lame leap like a deer, and the

tongue too long si - lent shouts for joy. Like a

stream in the des - ert is the Lord. Like a Lord.

116   Battle Song

Words and Music by
Ken Young

Psalm 144:1-8

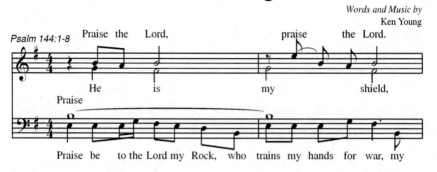

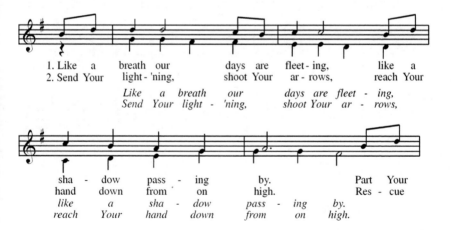

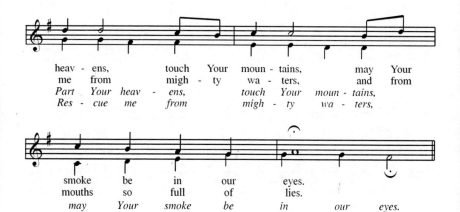

heav - ens,   touch Your moun - tains,   may Your
me from   migh - ty wa - ters,   and from
Part Your heav - ens,   touch Your moun - tains,
Res - cue me from   migh - ty wa - ters,

smoke be in our eyes.
mouths so full of lies.
may Your smoke be in our eyes.
and from mouths so full of lies.

117 Some May Trust in Chariots

Psalm 20:7

Words and Music by
Lynn DeShazo

Some may trust in hors - es, some may trust in char-i-ots, but we will trust in the

name of our God.   In the name   of Je - sus   our sal - va - tion lies,
By the blood   of Je - sus   sins are washed a - way,

D.C. al Fine

He will hear from heav - en   to   an - swer ev - 'ry   cry.
Sing for joy   to God, our strength, His   ban - ner we will   wave.

Some may trust in hors - es, some may trust in char-i-ots, but we will trust in the

Fine

name of our God.   We will trust   in Him.   We will trust   in Him.

Arranged by Ken Young

118   Tablet of Your Heart

Words and Music by
Ken Young

Proverbs 7

My son, *(my son,)* stop and lis - ten; guard my

teach - ings as the ap - ple of your eye. Bind

them *(bind them)* on your fing - er, write them down on the tab - let of your

heart, your heart, write them down on the tab - let of your heart.

1. There's a path, *(there's a path,)* nev-er take it, down a street
2. With smooth words, *(with smooth words,)* so per-sua - sive, she will lead

119 Be Thou My Vision

Philippians 3:7-9

Irish Folk Hymn/Words by
Mary E. Byrne & Ken Young

1. Be Thou my vi - sion, O Lord of my heart;
2. Rich - es I heed not, nor man's emp - ty praise;
3. Lord, I come search - ing for words to ex - press,

Bless - ed Re - deem - er and Sav - ior Thou art,
Thou my in - her - it - ance, now and al - ways:
My a - dor - a - tion of Thy ho - li - ness.

Thou my best thought, by day or by night,
Thou and Thou on - ly, first in my heart,
I am not wor - thy to look on Thy face,

Wak - ing or sleep - ing, Thy pres - ence my light.
High King of heav - en, my trea - sure Thou art.
I would be worth - less were it not for Thy grace.

Arranged by Ken Young

120 Blessed Heart

Matthew 5:8

Words and Music by
Ken Young

Ooh...

Bless-ed heart that comes from God, sel-dom

Faith forged thru the fi - re of the Spir-

Bless-ed are the pure in heart,

Help - ing hands, such sweet de - vo - tion, life spent in ser-

Ooh, *(Ah on Ten. solo)*

A tribute to Eugene Goudeau

D.S. and end with Sop. solo

Bless- ed heart giv - ing glo - ry to the King, bless - ed heart lift - ed up on an - gels' wings; Sing - ing prais - es to the Fa - ther with a voice that nev - er fails, walk - ing hand in hand with Je - sus with a smile a- cross his face.

Til My Faith Becomes Sight 121

1 Corinthians 13:12

Words and Music by
Dennis L. Jernigan

1. Bread of Life, pure Liv-ing Wa-ter, Lov-er of my soul,
2. Lamb of God, dear hope of glo-ry, Sav-ior cru-ci-fied,
(D.C.) Pre-cious ho-ly Lord and King so full of love and grace.

In my weak-ness be my strength to reach the fin-al goal.
By Your blood I am re-deemed my debt now sat-is- fied.
Tho I live or tho I die I rest in Your em- brace!

Tho they slay me, tho I fall; in dark-ness You are light, Je-sus.

I will keep my eyes on You til my faith be-comes sight. Oh,

Arranged by Sarah Bandy

122 Jesus Is Coming

Words and Music by
Ken Young

1 Thess.4:13-17; 2 Pet.3:3-10

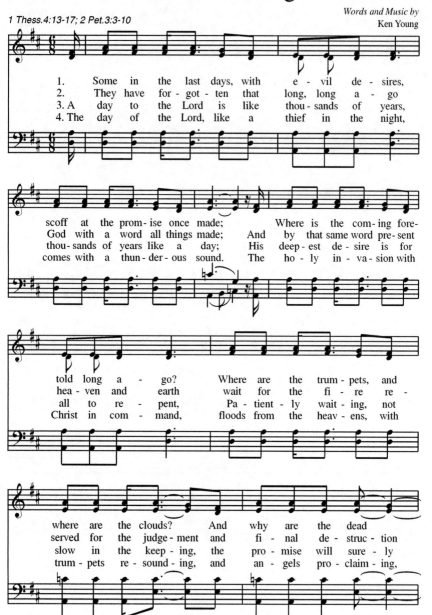

1. Some in the last days, with e - vil de - sires,
2. They have for - got - ten that long, long a - go
3. A day to the Lord is like thou - sands of years,
4. The day of the Lord, like a thief in the night,

scoff at the prom - ise once made; Where is the com - ing fore-
God with a word all things made; And by that same word pre - sent
thou - sands of years like a day; His deep - est de - sire is for
comes with a thun - der - ous sound. The ho - ly in - va - sion with

told long a - go? Where are the trum - pets, and
hea - ven and earth wait for the fi - re re -
all to re - pent, Pa - tient - ly wait - ing, not
Christ in com - mand, floods from the heav - ens, with

where are the clouds? And why are the dead
served for the judge - ment and fi - nal de - struc - tion
slow in the keep - ing, the pro - mise will sure - ly
trum - pets re - sound - ing, and an - gels pro - claim - ing,

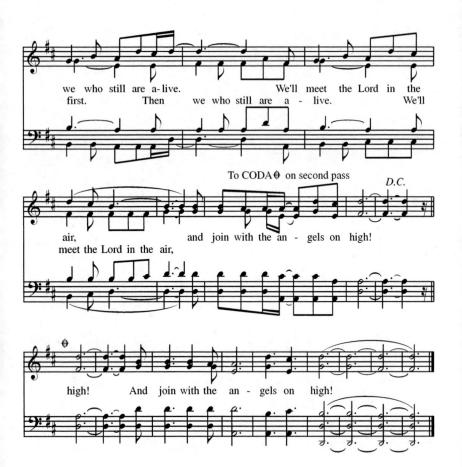

123 Let the Walls Come Down

Ephesians 2:15,16

Words and Music by
Jon Mohr

Ah,

Ah,

Ooh.

Ooh,

1. All through-out this spir-it realm a
2. Walls not born of gov-ern-ment, nor
(Lyrics for verses 3 & 4 on last page.)

fear - ful bat - tle ra - ges, the fates of men and na - tions hang sus-
strife a - mid the na - tions, but walls with-in our church - es, and be-

pend - ed in the fray. Walls de-signed by sa - tan in the
tween de - nom - i - na - tions. Stones of dry tra-di-tion carved in

Arranged by Ken Young

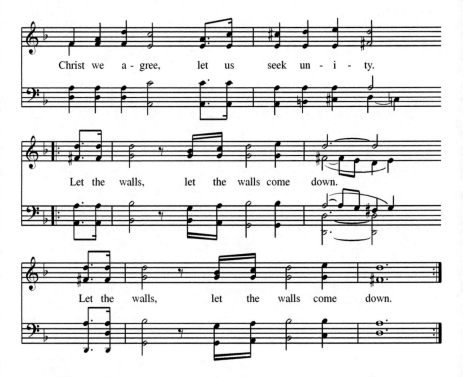

Christ we a - gree, let us seek un - i - ty.

Let the walls, let the walls come down.

Let the walls, let the walls come down.

3. The body weak and powerless, crippled by division,
The victim of a tragic and most cruel civil war.
Brother fighting brother over culture and tradition,
While countless lost and dying lie as casualties of war.

4. It's time to end the foolishness of warring with each other,
And kneel in true repentance that our union be restored.
May we then as brothers rally round the cross of Jesus,
And carry on with diligence the mission of our Lord!

124 Make Us One

John 17:20-23

Words and Music by
Ken Young

Ho - ly Spir - it, Heav- 'n - ly Dove,
Ho - ly Spir - it, Heav'n - ly

fill our hearts with Your heav - 'n - ly love.
Dove, fill our hearts with heav'n - ly

Make us one, make us one,
love. Make us one, make us
Make us one,

like the Fa - ther, and the Spir - it, and the
one

Son, make us one.

In this dark and vio - lent world there is a war that rag - es on, for the hearts of the be - liev - ers whom the Lord has called as one. We will take our stand to - ge - ther for the glo - ry of the cross, and the walls that have di - vid - ed us will crum - ble as the sound of praise a - gain is heard with one voice.

D.C. al Fine

125 - SCRIPTURE INDEX

127 - TOPICAL INDEX

129 - GENERAL INDEX

– NOTES –

– NOTES –